IT'S A NEW DAY

(poems for young brothas and sistuhs)

by

SONIA SANCHEZ

bp

Broadside Press   Detroit, Michigan

This book is dedicated to
DR. WILFRED CARTEY

First Edition
First Printing
Copyright © Sonia Sanchez 1971
All Rights Reserved

Back Cover Photograph: Ed Sherman

Cover and illustrations: Ademola Olugebefola, *Olori My Son,*
Reprinted courtesy of the Weusi Nyumba Ya Sanaa Gallery, New York
ISBN Cloth: 0-910296-68-5 $4.00
ISBN Paperback: 0-910296-60-X $1.25
LCN: 72-155311

Manufactured in the United States of America

CONTENTS

4

SET 1

Cuz we be black women
lovers of children . . . .

      to Marani and Mangu Weusi
      to Anita
      to Kenny
      Words for: Kali and Poochie
                  Geoffrey and Stephanie Hamilton

to Morani/Mungu

As-Salaam-Alaikum my black princes
the morning awaits u.
                        the world
awaits yo/young/blackness
sun/children
                of our tomorrow.
Here is my hand
                black/warriors of
our dreams.
                it is soft as the
blue/nite that covered yo/
blackness
                till day began its
morning talk.
                it is hard as
the strength u gather from
yo/father's words pouren
from his mouth like thunder
over a dry land.
                        but i am
here to love u my princes.
                            to gather
up yo/insides
                and make them
smile dreams.
                for u my loves
will be the doers.
                        and yo/deeds

will run red with ancient songs
hat play a continuous chant of
t's a new day.
                        it's a new new new day
            It's A NEW DAY!

As-Salaam-Alaikum
     young princes.
                        the world
awaits yo/young/blackness

to Anita

     high/yellow/black/girl
     walken like the sun u be.
     move on even higher.
                        those who
     laugh at yo/color
                        have not moved
     to the blackness we be about
     cuz as Curtis Mayfield be sayen
     we people be darker than blue
                        and quite a few
     of us be yellow
                        all soul/shades of
     blackness.
                        yeah. high/yellow/black/girl
     walk yo/black/song
            cuz some of us
                be hearen yo/sweet/music.

to Kenny

you are holy
young black God
as you reconstruct pyramids for our minds
as you interrupt our coca-cola lives
and turn them into a satellite
of black stars.
you are what the prophets saw
young manchild.
ancient as memory.

Words for Kali and Poochie

Blow our country a life color
you the children of jazz.
Roberta Flack yo/way
in and out of sermons
for soon you begin
              the Black Rhythm of Life
wailing past
    America's supermarket civilization.
go on now.
    sing us yo/riffs that will change the
direction of planets
             you baaaddDD/young/rhythms.
we hear you
        smile a new season
        and Bless The Day We Found You.

9

Words for Geoffrey
and Stephanie Hamilton

History has made this time for you.
that the final result be you
lyrical children of non-poetic times
is not the point.

                    you are. we have
thought you to be. and you come
lighting our underground minds

                              disturbing the trash
of cavish nine to five lives.
you are our poems
a cascading sound of rhyme and meter.
and when you enter into the streets and
walk yo earthquake walks
we live.

SET 2

And we be singen
teachen new songs to our children . . . .

       city songs
       don't wanna be
       just wanna be
       It's a New Day
       to P. J. (2 yrs old who sed write a poem
               for me in Portland, Oregon)

City Songs

dope pushers dope pushers
  git outa our parks
  we come to slide on slides
  climb the monkey bars

don't need yo/ dope
  to make us git high
  the swings will take us
  way up in the sky.

dope pushers dope pushers
  u ain't no friend
  no matter how you smile
  and always pretend

cuz we know nowadays
  black is a baaddDD groove
  and dope is a trick bag
  for fools fools fools

dope pushers dope pushers
  offa our street
  cuz one of these days
  you gonna meet

some together black men
  who'll show you the score
  and you won't be standing round
  tempting us no mo

dope pushers dope pushers
   change while you can
   it's nation/builden/time
   for black people in every land

so c'mon. c'mon. brothas
   run fas as u can
   and be what u must be
   sun people in a black land.

dope pushers dope pushers
   git back, git back
   cuz to git ahead today
   you gots to be black. black. black.

—Sonia Sanche
   1971

don't wanna be

don't wanna be
no pimp
    cuz pimps hate me and you
    they mommas, women, sistuhs too
    u name it, any hate will do

don't wanna be no pimp no mo
don't wanna be no pimp no mo

don't wanna be
no numbers runner
    cuz runners promise an uptown hit
    while downtown wite/boys just sit & sit
    while counten millions of four bits

don't wanna be no numbers runner no mo
don't wanna be no numbers runner no mo

don't wanna be
no junkie
    cuz junkies kill theyselves, you and me
    sticken needles in they arms, legs, an knee
    while robben our black community

don't wanna be no junkie no mo
don't wanna be no junkie no mo

Just wanna be
        a/Reverend/Cleage/man
        a/Minister/Farrakhan/man
        a/sun/people/Imamu/man
        an/Elijah/Muhammad/Messenger/man

wanna be
        a/blk/man
        a/loven/my blk/woman/man
        a/standen/still/father/man
        a/Constant/TCBing/black man

it gots to beeeEEE. yeah. yeah. yeah. yeah. yeah.
it gots to beeeEEE. yeah. yeah. yeah. yeah. yeah.

It's a New Day

we gon be
    outa sight black/men
    gon be part/
                panther
        gon be all Minister Farrakhan
            gon rap like RAP
    gonna teach like Elijah
        gon rule like Nyerere
            gon believe like King believed
            gonna be TCB/ing black men
as we walk in our red/yellow/suns

we gon be some
            beautiful/black/women
    gon move like the queens we be
    gon be full/
                time MUSLIM women
    gon be strong as sojourner
    gon be gentle as
                sister clotelle's smile
    gon be the poetry of gwendolyn's words
    gon be the green south of fannie lou hamer
gonna be warm as an african nite
while walken like songs

we gon be some badddDDD people
    just you wait and see
we gon be some badddDDD people
    just you wait and see . . . . . .

to P. J. (2 yrs old who sed write a poem for me in Portland, Oregon)

if i cud ever write a
poem as beautiful as u
little 2/yr/old/brotha,
i wud laugh, jump, leap
up and touch the stars
cuz u be the poem i try for
each time i pick up a pen and paper.
u. and Morani and Mungu
be our blue/blk/stars that
will shine on our lives and
makes us finally BE.
if i cud ever write a poem as beautiful
as u, little 2/yr/old/brotha,
poetry wud go out of bizness.

SET 3

and we will be . . . .

> when we come
> safari
> we can BE

Safari

Cmon yall
       on a safari
into our plantation/jungle/minds
and let us catch the nigger
roamen inside of us.
       let us hang
       our white   aping
       actions
       on walls
       with signs that
       announce the last
       of our nigger thoughts
       is dead.
       only blackness
       runs in our veins.
Cmon yall
       follow me on a new african safari
       and LIVE!

When we come

When we come
riden our green horses
against the tenement dust,
when we come, tall as waves,
holden our black/brown/
high yellow/tomorrows,
then you will hear young hooves
thunderen in space
and we will rise with
rainbows from the sea
to silence
our yesterday blues

when we come
riden our green breath
against the morning sky.

WE CAN BE

we can be anything we want
for we are the young ones
walken without footprints
moven our bodies in tune
to songs

        echoen us. the beautiful
black ones.

        recently born.

                walken new
                rhythms
leaven behind us a tap dancer's dream
of sunday nite ed sullivan shows.
WE WILL BE

        ALL that we want
for we are the young ones
bringen the world to a Black Beginnen.

SET 4

*cuz we be a new people in a new land
and it will be ours* . . . .

    we're not learnen to be paper boys
and it will be ours

We're not learnen to be paper boys
(for the young brothas who sell
Muhammad Speaks)

we're not learnen to be paper boys
with a one/block/route.
America is full of paper boys
collecten dimes and quarters for
a five/dollar a week/American Dream.
we're sellen truth
and our route is the mind of blk people.
we are men goen the way of the
new man spreaden the
knowledge of self and truth.
Let us recite out loud our blk/praises to Elijah Muhammad
Let us recite out loud our blk/love for our selves.

And it will be ours

we are a new people
look at us walk. we walken
A New Walk. Its beat is the sound of Elijah
hurryen us to new frontiers.
we be a new people in a new land.

we wear a new look
look at the style we wear. our clothes
demand your look. respect. for they tell
the land that a new people's garments
flow on the earth.
we be a new people in a new land.

our talk is new. it be
original talk always prefaced by
As-Salaam-alaikum (a greeting of peace)
for how else should we begin the day
save with peace for our people in a new land.
we be a new people in a new land.

we are a mixture of the old and new.
a new western man of ancient wisdom
openen the door of the world
while moven on a new land
in a new way.
we be a new people in a new land.

our leader is new. a man of the land
bringen us holy words for him all
praises are due Allah who came
bearen the truth of Islam for this
original man in this new land who
is multiplyen out loud.

and if we listen. ahhhh yes. and
if we listen. we new people
in this new land will be the rulers.
and it will be ours. and it will be ours.

If you like this book . . .

you will like some of our other books listed on the inside front cover or on our flyers. You can order them conveniently by mailing this order form.

I enclose $_____ for the books listed below. (Add 25 cents for postage and handling.)

Author	Title	Price	No. of Copies	Total

Postage and Handling _____.25

Grand Total $_____

Name_____

Address_____

City_____State_____Zip_____

Mail check or money order to

BROADSIDE PRESS

Dept. M.O., 12651 Old Mill Place   Detroit, Michigan 48238